D0585581

pohutukawa

pohutukawa

TREE OF AOTEAROA

Text by Linda Bercusson
Compiled by Jacinda Torrance

Project Crimson

Supported by Carter Holt Harvey Limited
& the Department of Conservation.

TANDEM PRESS

First published in 1998 by
TANDEM PRESS
2 Rugby Road
Birkenhead
Auckland 10
New Zealand

Cover and book design by Jacinda Torrance
Typesetting by Jacinda Torrance

Printed and bound by Sands Printing
Group, Australia

Special thanks to:
Chris Hegan, Alison Henry, Gordon
Hosking, Bret McKay, Stanley Palmer,
Philip Simpson and Graeme Torrance for
their help in the production of this book.

Linda Bercusson spent several years as staff
journalist for the Department of Conservation
in Auckland. She was journalist in residence
for the New Zealand Antarctic Programme
and has a long association with pohutukawa
and rata through her work for Project Crimson.
Other assignments have taken her to San Diego,
Vanuatu and into the Tasman sea with the
Greenpeace campaign against driftnetting.

Jacinda Torrance has worked as a graphic
designer for eight years. She has been involved
in many projects for the Department of
Conservation and Greenpeace.

Contents

Pohutukawa

Gnarled trunks. Prehensile roots grasping stubbornly to crumbling cliffs. Flaming blooms. Christmas. Summer days.

The pohutukawa has such power in the New Zealand psyche that the mention of its name is enough to set minds drifting towards snoozing on the beach under the shade of spreading branches, long, lazy days and picnics.

Its blossoms make this famous native one of our most popular and easiest to spot and they are now found well outside their natural growing range, as far afield as South Africa and North America.

At the moment, pohutukawa are plentiful, but they are under constant attack. The coastal forests that once fringed Northland are long gone and, although there are still thousands of mature trees to be seen, few seedlings are reaching maturity.

This is the story of one of the great trees of New Zealand — of its place on the land and in people's hearts, of the threats it faces and a country's determination to safeguard its future.

Left: Little Barrier Island.

No ordinary tree

Few native plants have moved so many people to stain page and canvas with such perfect or purple allusions.

The pohutukawa features in the earliest oral histories and colonial Christmas celebrations, both cultures venerating its spirituality, strength and beauty. For Maori it is one of the chiefly trees or rakaurangatira.

GRAEME TORRANCE

Left: Young Nafi Pole's dream Christmas present is now an Auckland landmark. After months of pestering, grandfather Halauafu crafted what is now Grey Lynn's most famous treehut. The two-storey whimsey, complete with beds, is not so much in the tree as around it, supporting its own weight. 'I didn't want to hurt the tree,' said Halauafu. 'There are no nails in the tree at all.'
PHOTO: CHRIS HEGAN

The *name* comes from the word 'hutukawa', a headdress of red feathers and 'po-' which has many meanings but can refer to the night or underworld. Governor George Grey interpreted this to mean the tree with the red adornment growing near the sea: 'Ko te hutukawa e tu ana i te taha o te wai'.[1]

Near Waiaro on the Port Jackson Road, Coromandel Peninsula.
Auckland War Memorial Museum.
Estate of Robin Morrison.
ROBIN MORRISON

Left: Otangimoana Bay, Lake Okataina.
CHRIS RUDGE, DEPARTMENT OF CONSERVATION

The pohutukawa in Maori tradition and folklore

In Arawa tradition, chief Tauninihi, on seeing the flame-fringed coast of Aotearoa, chucked his red feather headdress (kura) into the sea, assuming better plumage was waiting for him when he landed. He was so disappointed the distant feathers were really fragile pohutukawa blooms that he went to retrieve his old headdress. In the meantime, a man called Mahina had picked up the feathered flotsam and refused to return it, saying it was drift kura. This is the basis of the Maori saying 'te kura pae a Mahina' or finders keepers.

Left: A cluster of pohutukawa blossoms.
BRET MCKAY

Right: Moss covered pohutukawa trunk on Urupukapuka Island in the Bay of Islands.
GRAEME TORRANCE

The red flowers not only become part of the mythical origins of the new homeland, but also point to the time of the Arawa waka's arrival. In another story, young Maori warrior Tawhaki climbed to heaven to find help avenging his father's death. The pohutukawa's crimson flowers are said to represent his blood after falling to his own death. There are many versions of this tale, but the meaning, according to anthropologist Margaret Orbell, established a key principle of human conduct, the ability to travel from the physical to the spiritual – earth to sky.

Many individual trees are tapu.
The most striking embodiment of this
is a small, scraggy pohutukawa clinging
to the edge of Muriwhenua or Lands End
(Cape Reinga). 'Te Reinga' is said to guard
the entrance to a secret cave through which
spirits of the dead pass on their way to the
next world. To say that someone has 'slid
down the pohutukawa root' is a lyrical
way of saying he has joined his ancestors.[2]

Grim, gaunt and weird
Adorned with strange fantastic arms
It stands: a silent beacon
To departing shades;
A leafy portal to the gates
Of dark and mystic worlds.

The Art Album of New Zealand Flora,
Sarah and Edward Featon, 1889.

Maori planted pohutukawa to mark the
burial place of chiefs, battlefields where
warriors died, or the birth of a chief's son.
They used the juice of its bark to reduce
inflammation and as a remedy for diarrhoea,
dysentery, gangrene and thrush. Chewing
the bark anaesthetised sore gums and
toothache, sometimes permanently by
killing the nerve. Sucking its nectar cured
a sore throat.

Above: Little Barrier Island.
BRET MCKAY

Right: 'Te Reinga' guards the entrance
to a secret cave at Muriwhenua.
ARNO GASTEIGER

Left: From *Captain
Cook's Florilegium*,
Plate 10 'Metrosideros
excelsa myrtaceae'.
Auckland City Libraries (NZ).
SYDNEY PARKINSON

Top right: Urupukapuka
Island in the Bay of Islands.
GRAEME TORRANCE

Below right: From *The Native
Flowers of New Zealand*,
Plate 29 'Pohutukawa
metrosideros tomentosa'.
Auckland City Libraries (NZ).
MRS CHARLES HETLEY

European settlement

European settlers were also quick
to appreciate the tree. In 1814, Reverend
Samuel Marsden celebrated Christmas at
Oihi beach in the Bay of Islands, introducing
the new Gospel to local Maori against
a backdrop of flowering pohutukawa.
Homesick immigrants readily embraced
the red blooms as their Christmas holly.
Shipbuilders, alerted to its qualities by
botanical explorers such as Sir Joseph
Banks, William Colenso and Thomas Kirk,
transformed the naturally curved limbs
of the pohutukawa into massive ribs for
sailing ships. The pohutukawa was not
only extremely durable but also resistant
to seaworms.

'It is a very valuable tree, especially for shipbuilding purposes, where its gnarled and crooked character make it highly serviceable for timber, knees, breast-hooks, etc; it is also used for making ship's blocks and for building piles. This wood presents a very handsome grain, a rich rose colour, and a high polish when worked up by the cabinetmaker, and choice pieces are in great demand.' *(William Colenso, 1868)*[3]

Shipbuilders readily transformed the pohutukawa's naturally curved limbs into massive ribs for sailing ships.
PHOTOS: BRET MCKAY

The botanists recognised the danger of over-exploitation and at different times issued early conservation warnings:

'The Pohutukawa … has contributed largely to the progress of this part of the colony, is without the benefit of protection, and has been in some cases recklessly cut down for firewood … Although confessedly difficult, it would seem not impracticable to prevent this wanton destruction of valuable timber, by legislative enactment; it is certainly desirable, in the interest of the miners them-selves, no less than in that of the colony at large.' (*Thomas Kirk, 1869*)[4]

Alfred Sharpe

One of the first to capture the pohutukawa's evocative personality on canvas was English émigré Alfred Sharpe. He was an early champion of all native trees but had a passion for pohutukawa. Sharpe was very vocal in his objections to the work of acclimatisation societies bent on introducing a host of animals and vegetation to remind them of home. In the upper branches of his 1876 watercolour of Takapuna beach's Te Urutapu (Sacred Grove) you can just make out a wasps' nest, some of what he called the 'vermin' threatening New Zealand's novel wilderness. Ironically, he later imported pohutukawa into New South Wales where he designed several parks.

Pohutukawa near the landing place below Lake Pupuke, Takapuna, 1876. Watercolour, Auckland Art Gallery Toi o Tamaki.
ALFRED SHARPE

Right: *Pohutukawa on a Cliff,
Whangaparaoa*, 1868.
Albumen on paper,
Auckland Art Gallery Toi o Tamaki.
JOHN KINDER

Laden limbs. Kiekie growing on twisted pohutukawa
at Waiwera with Mahurangi Island in the distance.

Pohutukawa and Island, Mahurangi, 1970.
Engraving and lithograph.
STANLEY PALMER

Left: Late sunlight on pohutukawa, Little Barrier Island.
BRET MCKAY

Contemporary culture

The sinuous tree, like its creeping roots over bare ground, has firmly rooted itself in modern culture too. The pohutukawa is part of an elite group of icons that can make experienced New Zealand travellers instantly pine for the beaches of home. For many New Zealanders it is synonymous with long summer holidays, days at the beach and shading sunburnt skin from even more damage.

But as with that other potent national symbol, the kiwi, long-term survival for pohutukawa still hangs in the balance.

Left: Mount Maunganui.
JOCELYN CARLIN

Right: St Heliers.
JOCELYN CARLIN

A game of kilikiti (Samoan cricket) on the
pohutukawa-lined beach at Maraetai.
JOCELYN CARLIN

Eric Lee-Johnson

Although Eric Lee-Johnson made his name in the 1940s and early 1950s as a landscape painter, his most lasting images survive in his photographs. He lived in and around Auckland for most of his life, imbuing natural objects like stones, seaweed, driftwood and trees with an often surreal quality. His passion, without doubt, was the pohutukawa, and he amassed a collection of more than 3000 images. These are now held in Te Papa, The Museum of New Zealand.

Negative no. CT.12212
Eric-Lee Johnson Collection,
Museum of New Zealand
Te Papa Tongarewa.
ERIC LEE JOHNSON

Coromandel Peninsula.
JOCELYN CARLIN

Pohutukawa, 1903-1915.
Oil on card,
Auckland Art Gallery Toi o Tamaki.
CLAUS EDWARD FRISTROM

'Pain and age are in these gnarled forms,
in bare roots, clutching at the earth,
knotting on the cliff-face, in tortured
branches, dark against the washed sky.'

The End of the Golden Weather, Bruce Mason

Left: East Cape, near Opotiki.
GRAEME MATTHEWS

31

Paritai Drive, Auckland.
Auckland War Memorial Museum.
Estate of Robin Morrison.
ROBIN MORRISON

Near Waiaro, Coromandel Peninsula.
Auckland War Memorial Museum.
Estate of Robin Morrison.
ROBIN MORRISON

Botany

Pohutukawa belong to the myrtle family (Myrtaceae) which is made up of about 3000 tropical and warm temperate trees, shrubs and vines. Eucalyptus, feijoas, cloves, guavas and bottlebrushes are a few family members supplying timber, fruit, spices and garden plants.

In New Zealand myrtles are represented by some of our best-known plants: rata, kanuka, manuka and some less familiar but nevertheless significant species like swamp maire and ramarama.

PHOTOS: BRET MCKAY

The tree is a member of the genus *Metro-sideros*, the iron hearted myrtles, a reference to its hard, very heavy, dark red heartwood. It is superbly adapted to its natural environment. The tiny seeds of this outstanding coastal character blow into the smallest of cracks; its leaves carry soft hairs to minimise water loss; its canopy, more horizontal than vertical, spreads weight through root-laden branches to resist the harshest storms.

Young trees on Little Barrier Island.
BRET MCKAY

Right: Great Barrier Island.
BRET MCKAY

According to Department of Conservation botanist Dr Philip Simpson, the pohutukawa's 'ancestor probably occupied the mobile islands of the south-west Pacific in early Tertiary time (the Paleocene, 65–55 million years ago), perhaps colonising the volcanic or sedimentary rocks as they emerged from the sea.

'This ability is still common to the Pacific species like Hawaii's ohia lehua, New Zealand's Kermadec Island pohutukawa and pohutukawa itself. But the ancestor has also given rise to modern species that have gone beyond the coastlines and entered the great forests of Aotearoa, creating towering trees and forest lianes. And so New Zealand has been important in both the origin and diversification of *Metrosideros*.'[1]

Unique design

The pohutukawa is uniquely designed for colonising bare lava. Its branches form large masses of aerial roots which, when they touch ground, take hold in the usually unstable rock. Individuals can live as long as 1000 years and as Philip Simpson says, every feature of the anatomy and physiology has to be extremely well adapted.

This makes him think this coastal tree has a higher ecological 'purpose', providing shelter in which other colonising plants can grow.

Aerial roots.
JACK HOBBS

Reproduce fast – you might not last

So goes the *Metrosideros* multiplication motto.

This nine-month-old seedling illustrates one of the keys to the genus' colonising plan – adaptability. In harsh, rocky sites, such as lava flows, very young plants can flower. Even though the location may not be viable for a full-grown specimen, the opportunity is taken as a staging post for reproduction.

This ability to colonise harsh sites through early flowering can sometimes be seen on the Hauraki Gulf's Rangitoto Island and is shared by West Coast southern rata and Tahitian and Hawaiian pohutukawa. Pohutukawa have also adapted to life in the city, anchoring themselves in cracks in chimneys, footpaths, brick walls and guttering.

PHOTO: BRET MCKAY

Northern coastal forest, large spreading tree often rupestral.
M. excelsa
(Pohutukawa)

Far northern warm temperate forest, initially epiphytic, medium canopy tree.
M. bartletti
(Bartlett's rata)

Warm temperate forest, initially epiphytic, becoming large emergent tree.
M. robusta
(Northern rata)

Subtropical island coastal forest, small tree forming clonal groves.
M. kermadecensis
(Kermadec Islands pohutukawa)

Subgenus *Metrosideros* trees. High Pacific Islands, Solomons, Lord Howe, Kermadec, New Caledonia, New Zealand.

Cool temperate montane to subantarctic forests, terrestrial or rupestral, small to large tree, sometimes shrub.
M. umbellata
(Southern rata)

Ancestral *Metrosideros*. Paleocene (65-55 million years ago) Greater New Zealand continent (including New Caledonia). Terrestrial trees.

Fleshy fruited subfamily Asia, Africa, America.

Subgenus *Mearnsia* vines. Borin Island, Philippines, New Guinea, New Caledonia, New Zealand.

Dry fruited subfamily. Australia **(*Eucalyptus*)**, SW Pacific.

Myrtaceae trees

Cretaceous birth of the flowering plant families 80 – 100 million years ago. Gondwanaland.

Kermadec and mainland

New Zealand has two forms of native pohutukawa: mainland (*M. excelsa*) and Kermadec pohutukawa (*M. kermadecensis*). The latter is endemic to Raoul Island, in the Kermadec group, 1000 kilometres north-east of New Zealand. The two species hybridise easily and conservationists take great care to ensure cuttings and seeds are grown from genetically pure *M. excelsa* stock.

Above: *Metrosideros kermadecensis*.
BRET MCKAY

Right: *Metrosideros excelsa*.
JACK HOBBS

Bark

Rough and stringy, forming a medium-thick, dry covering capable of protecting the tree from drought; an excellent surface for its own aerial roots and roots of epiphytes (epiphytes store water for themselves and their host).

Habit

A massive spreading crown; wider than tall, moulds to coastal wind and slope and spreads weight over unstable ground; canopy shelters root systems on bare rock.

Root system

Roots form from trunks and branches; able to grow in air over surfaces as they search for crevices, pockets of soil and moisture.

Seedling

Primary root supplemented by adventitious roots growing from the stems to aid creeping over and attachment to surfaces and entering crevices.

Wood

Dense and strong, as needed to withstand wind damage and drought; slow growing.

Flowers

Spectacular crimson colour and abundant nectar attract birds and geckos.

Flower buds terminal (beyond leaves) so flowers are conspicuous.

Flowering is more or less uniform on a single tree, but flowering time is staggered over a population, ensuring through pollination the maintenance of genetic diversity needed in a colonising species.

Fruit and seed

Capsule opens to enable wind dispersal of seed.

Seeds are small for easy dispersal and entry into rock crevices, an ideal strategy for a rock colonising, coastal plant.

Leaves and shoots

Dormant leaf and floral buds protected by bud scales against damage from cold, salt and abrasion.

Leaves live for two years and can be quickly replaced if lost in a wind storm.

Leaves are hairy when young. When mature the hair on the upper surface is replaced by a tough, shiny coat of wax. Protects against drought, salt, glare. Dense soft hairs remain underneath to reduce water loss from the leaf's tiny pores.

Shoots divide into two branches from opposite, upper buds so that the system spreads widely.

FROM PHILIP SIMPSON'S PAPER *BIODIVERSITY AND POHUTUKAWA*

A giant pohutukawa
at Auckland's Parnell
Gardens.
JACK HOBBS

Pohutukawa and the forest ecosystem

Picture-postcard perfect and brimming
with life. A healthy pohutukawa feeds, houses
and supports a staggering number of plants,
animals and insects.

Although bird and insect life on the mainland
has declined dramatically since humans arrived,
the pohutukawa maintains its basic ecological
survival pattern, sequential flowering (and
therefore nectar flow) over a long period of
time. Honeyeaters like tui, bellbirds (extinct
in Northland) and stitchbirds (now gone from
the mainland) feast on the tree's vaguely salty
nectar as do pekapeka, our native short-tailed
bats.

47

Geckos feeding on the nectar
of pohutukawa blossoms.
TONY WHITAKER

Right: Pied shags roosting in pohutukawa branches.
BRET MCKAY

Geckos (Common, Pacific and Duvaucel's) flock to newly opened flowers like bargain hunters to a sale. Ecologist and herpetologist Tony Whitaker has observed up to five geckos feeding on a single flowerhead. Pollen also clings to the heads, undersurface and feet of these tiny lizards, suggesting they also play a small pollinating role.[1]

Shags and white-faced herons roost and nest in canopies, bats colonise split branches and crevices. Saddlebacks nest in holes in the trunk and the tree's flaky bark is home to an impressive number of insects and spiders. Weevils, beetles, flies, moths and scale insects feed on foliage, bark, fruit and the twig and leaf litter around the trunk. Just above the strand line (extreme high water mark), tough little snails survive in the decaying litter.

Urban street problems

A bird in the hand may be worth two in the bush, but a cat in the tree is priceless, especially if you are trying to scare away 7000 of the feathered creatures.

After 15 years of trying, the Wellington City Council finally found a way to stop 5000 starlings and 2000 sparrows roosting in the 55-year-old pohutukawa outside the Wellington Club on the Terrace. Protected from the northerly wind, the tree had become a comfortable retreat for the birds who clung tenaciously to their membership privileges. Unfortunately for the building's tenants, the morning trek across the footpath and past the tree was often a slippery job.

The secret weapon was a red silhouette of a cat's head with clear marble eyes which glint in the light as the cutout spins on its string. In hindsight it may seem an obvious ploy, but it has taken years of strategising to reach this stage.

Over the years the council had called in the Fire Service which hosed the big tree with water; connected a fine spray to the tree's crown in the hope that continuous drenching might deter the birds – unfortunately the water started to undermine the footpath; stretched a heavy net over the whole tree – the birds crawled up underneath and tangled themselves; stretched a fine net over the tree which ended up falling to pieces; and set off loud alarms which upset the sparrows but not the starlings.

The swinging cat silhouettes are an Australian invention designed to scare birds out of vineyards. So far the experiment has succeeded. The starlings have flown elsewhere, while the sparrows now live happily along Lambton Quay.

What's hot and what's rot

Fungi are everywhere. Some attack their host, but many root fungi (mycorrhiza) are essential to the plant's well-being. Although how is not fully understood, they effectively increase the nutrient available to the plant in poor soils. While many fungi remain unseen below the ground, others reveal themselves in their fruiting bodies above ground. Whenever you see clusters of mushrooms beneath a tree canopy, you are usually seeing the tip of an extensive underground fungal iceberg.

Of the 80 fungi associated with pohutukawa, few hinder the tree's growth.

Another function of fungus is to break down organic matter. The common *Gymnopilus spectabilis* is one of a handful of flashy fungi found on fallen pohutukawa trunks and limbs.

Gymnopilus spectabilis.
PETER BUCHANAN, LANDCARE RESEARCH

Pohutukawa honey

The whitest honey in the world with a delicate hint of salt, according to apiarist Mike Stuckey. For more than 40 years he has been travelling back and forth to Rangitoto Island, collecting the pohutukawa's bounty. He averages about 12 tonnes of honey a year with his 200 hives and is looking to increase production now that possums have been eliminated from the pohutukawa forest.

Left: Native bees gather mainly pollen from Rangitoto's pohutukawa, leaving the nectar for the honeybees. New Zealand has about 40 species of native bee; small and solitary, they are quite common but easily missed.

PHOTOS: BRET MCKAY

Vanishing glory

For all its adaptability and talent
for surviving on impossibly rocky ground
and vertical hillsides, the species is in trouble.
The pohutukawa forests which once formed
a continuous coastal fringe north of a line
from Kawhia to Gisborne are unlikely to
be seen again. The reasons for this are many.

Top of the list is the Australian brushtail
possum which devours the trees' leaves and
tender young shoots and buds as if they
were marsupial ice-cream. Then there are
insects, disease and human development.

Australian brushtail possum, *Trichosarus vulpecula.*
ARNO GASTEIGER

Left: Dead pohutukawa at Cape Brett in the Bay of Islands.
KENNEDY WARNE

Exacerbating the pohutukawa's predicament is its sensitivity to fire and inability to regenerate in pasture grasses or weeds where stock is present. Fire, historically one of the most common methods of clearing land, is anathema to many myrtles, but even a light grass fire at the base can kill a mature pohutukawa. The tree's roots, designed to spread over rocks, are also easily disturbed by trampling, whether by grazing animals, cars or people. Its tiny seeds do not have enough food reserves to last long in soil, nor push a young sapling through the matted roots of grass or kikuyu.

A 1989 Forest Research Institute investigation into the health of *Metrosideros excelsa* found that pastoral farming had eliminated more than 90 percent of coastal pohutukawa stands. The tree has entirely disappeared in many areas along the west coast of Northland.[1]

'Perhaps the fundamental reason for pohutukawa declining,' says botanist Dr Philip Simpson, 'is that it is an island plant, unused to sharing its space with large animals.

'For the most part the ecological processes that have operated for millions of years, crafting a finely adapted living edge to the land, have been disrupted. A prison of geriatric trees has replaced a dynamic ecosystem.'[2]

Cooks Bay, Coromandel Peninsula.
GRAEME MATTHEWS

Grazing stock easily
disturb sensitive roots.
Coromandel Peninsula.
ARNO GASTEIGER

Bird versus tree

The pohutukawa forest on Rangitoto Island, off the coast of metropolitan Auckland, illustrates a unique set of human-animal-plant relationships, according to Dr Philip Simpson. 'On the west face of the island is a black-backed gull breeding colony. Here, hundreds of gulls nest each year out in open lava fields where they probably feel a sense of security from potential enemies.'

The result of such a large number of birds concentrating in one area is a mass of plant life totally unrelated to pohutukawa ecosystems. 'Because of the rich nutrient they bring to the area through their droppings, the black lava has become clothed in a dense mat of lichen, moss and liverworts. The gulls also bring nesting material in from surrounding mainland areas and also food for their chicks. Much of this is scavenged from urban waste and the nests are littered with bones from lamb chops, pieces of plastic, metal and even coins.

'More spectacularly, each nest is surrounded by herbaceous vegetation which does not grow naturally on the lava. Most of the species are common introduced weeds or garden escapes.'

Another byproduct of the nutrient bonanza is the untypically dense canopy leaf growth on the surrounding pohutukawa. 'The leaves are probably also more nutritious than is usual and are highly palatable to possums. The result is that the gull colony attracts hoards of possums and they, in turn, browse the pohutukawa so severely that many have died. The newly open ground becomes swamped with weeds.'

Over the last few years, the Department of Conservation has eradicated possums from the island and in time a healthy canopy of pohutukawa will inhibit light and nutrient-demanding weeds.

Above: Southern black-backed gull, *Larus dominicanus dominicanus*.
DEPARTMENT OF CONSERVATION

Right: Tamaki Drive, Auckland.
ARNO GASTEIGER

Pohutukawa – a South African weed

Stands of impenetrable pohutukawa. It may be a New Zealand dream, but in the dense fynbos vegetation at the south-western tip of South Africa, the species is listed as a serious alien invader.

Pohutukawa are colonising the eastern half of Betty's Bay, an area rich in native plants which had escaped invasive foreigners because of the peaty soil. However, in the last eight years thousands of *M. excelsa* have taken root. In one area, Cape Town University botanist Dave Richardson counted as many as 6250 first-year seedlings per square metre.

'At one site, (we called this 'the nightmare scenario plot') we counted 130 saplings up to two-and-a-half metres tall in one four-square metre study area.

'Although the pohutukawa is not likely to invade huge areas, it certainly poses a severe threat to biodiversity in the region.'

Richardson is uncertain why pohutukawa numbers have exploded in the last eight years and will be continuing his research. In the meantime, local residents are hard at it pulling out young trees and seedlings.

Right: Little Barrier Island.
BRET MCKAY

Fighting back –
Project Crimson

Disturbed by Forest Research Institute's findings, Northland Department of Conservation officer Gerry Brackenbury and staff from New Zealand Forest Products (now Carter Holt Harvey) came up with the idea of creating a community-based project to help pohutukawa. In 1990 the Project Crimson Trust came to life.

The Trust's work has captured the hearts of thousands of New Zealanders who have given their time and energy to hundreds of community and school projects.

Replanting the Kaipara coast.
LINDA BERCUSSON

Left: Bumble bee on pohutukawa.
BRET MCKAY

Gathering seeds, growing seedlings and nurturing a new generation of trees are vital parts of Project Crimson's work. So far, more than 100,000 pohutukawa and rata have been grown and planted with the Trust's help.

Much of Project Crimson's stock is raised in prison nurseries. The 1992 scheme began on a small scale in a joint venture with Auckland's Paremoremo Prison.

Several other prisons have since joined in, including Kaitoke and Waikeria. This unlikely partnership provides sound horticultural training for inmates while Project Crimson is able to supply community groups, schools and councils with a guaranteed stock of quality, locally sourced trees. The remainder of the trees are grown by volunteers and the CCS nursery in Auckland.

Through Carter Holt Harvey's sponsorship the Trust has also funded the publication of a comprehensive pohutukawa and tree rata bibliography, and an investigation into which fungi are specific to these species. Other scientific projects include research into chemically synthesising the scent of the wood rose (*Dactylanthus taylorii*), one of the possums' favourite foods, to see if it can be used to bait the insatiable import; a hunt for the southernmost naturally occurring stand of *Metrosideros excelsa* in Taranaki; examining DNA to determine provenance variation; and a study into why only 9.5 percent of pohutukawa seeds are fertile.

Otangimoana Bay, Lake Okataina.
CHRIS RUDGE, DEPARTMENT OF CONSERVATION

The Cape Brett possum fence

GRAEME TORRANCE

The summer of 1995 brought a rare sight to this part of Northland – blooming pohutukawa. After years of watching the trees deteriorate locals joined forces with Project Crimson, the Department of Conservation and the Northland Regional Council to build the country's first effective solar-powered electric possum fence. The two-and-a-half kilometre barrier stretches across the Cape Brett Peninsula, through conservation reserve and land owned by the 3B2 Iwi Trust.

During the many months of preparatory work possums, goats and rabbits were culled from inside the area to be fenced, a track cut and archaeological surveys undertaken. The changes since the first possum control work has been dramatic, leading to semi light-hearted complaints from possum hunters who now struggle through regenerating undergrowth.

If the restoration of the coastal forest is successful this part of Cape Brett may become a 'mainland island', an area of the mainland constantly monitored and protected to create an island-like ecological enclave which can one day provide a haven for threatened plants and animals.

With its pohutukawa campaign progressing well, Project Crimson decided in 1997 to include the besieged tree rata in its work, as they face many of the same threats as their cousins.

Project Crimson is a conservation success story. It has managed to unite often disparate groups and taken a diverse, pragmatic approach to rescuing the species.

Above: Bartlett's rata.
EWEN CAMERON

The tree rata

Northern rata

(Metrosideros robusta) is well-known throughout North Island forests, and extends southwards as far as Hokitika. It usually begins life as a perching plant, high in the forest's canopy. This forest giant is one of New Zealand's tallest flowering trees, with a lower trunk of up to three metres in diameter.

Bartlett's rata

(Metrosideros bartlettii) was discovered in 1975 in a forest remnant near Cape Reinga. Only 30 adult trees are known in just three bush remnants and the species is listed as endangered. Its white flowers and pale papery bark make it unique among this country's rata.

Southern rata

(Metrosideros umbellata) is the most widely spread New Zealand rata – from small trees on high Northland and Coromandel outcrops to the subantarctic Auckland Islands where it forms the country's southernmost forests.

A kea surveys his territory from the top of a Southern rata.
ROGAN COLBOURNE,
DEPARTMENT OF CONSERVATION

Left: Northern rata.
BRET MCKAY

Growing pohutukawa –
Project Crimson's guide
to growing healthy trees

The key is knowing in advance where you want to plant – there are geographical and ecological considerations which must be taken into account. From thinking about it to planting out is a two or three year process which starts with finding the right parents. If your main objective is to grow a tree in your garden, look for a specimen with characteristics which you find appealing. Do you want a broad, spreading habit or a tree which naturally tends to grow upright? Obviously, you will be looking for healthy, heavy flowering specimens. Most importantly: don't bring in seed from another part of the country.

JACK HOBBS

Left: Medlands Beach, Great Barrier Island.
BRET MCKAY

The Department of Conservation has mapped a number of ecological districts within pohutukawa's natural range which vary in size. Each district has its own ecological identity, and the integrity of each population is already under assault from introduced and horticultural specimens. Even identical-looking trees from different areas will have different genetic identities.

Pick a number of trees in a single location

A 'location' can be hard to define – it might be a peninsula, a group of two or three beaches with similar aspect and conditions, an island or a stretch of sand dunes. Don't just go for the trees which are easy to get to. Take the trouble to look around to ensure a good range of selection.

Select a similar ecosystem

If your target area is a south-facing hilly region with a tendency to frost, then large, spreading trees from a north-facing beach site may not do too well there. Influences to be aware of include rainfall, soil type, proximity to the coast, general topography and wind.

Above: Pohutukawa forest, the Poor Knights.
ROD MORRIS, DEPARTMENT OF CONSERVATION

Left: Little Barrier Island.
BRET MCKAY

Pohutukawa blooms come in many shades,
from pale yellow to brilliant red.
PHOTOS: (ABOVE) JACK HOBBS;
(RIGHT) J. GARDINER, DEPARTMENT
OF CONSERVATION

Identify attractive, healthy trees

Attractive trees are desirable, and the flowers are an important food source for nectar-eating birds. This does not mean only those trees which are flowering heavily when you find them. Look for good trees which show signs of having already flowered, or trees which still have lots of buds, and mark those as well. A forest of trees all flowering two weeks before Christmas is not much use to tui, kaka and bell-birds who rely on a long flowering period.

Pohutukawa flowers come in many colours, from pale yellow to pink. Although these trees have a novelty value, the interests of conservation are better served if only crimson flowering trees are propagated.

Ensure that each tree is genetically 'pure'

This can be difficult to ascertain, but following some basic rules will increase your chances.

- Eliminate any trees which are not growing naturally regardless of appearances, avoid trees growing in or near cultivated areas such as gardens, council picnic sites and parks.

- Ensure that your trees are distant from species which could hybridise with them (for example, Kermadec pohutukawa or rata). This effectively means a spot at least five or six kilometres from gardens, picnic sites or forests where rata might be growing. Checking out a radius of that size is quite an undertaking, but at least keep an eye out for sources of cross-pollination.

- Avoid roadside plants (always of unknown origin).

Pohutukawa beside the main road at
Thornton's Bay, Coromandel Peninsula.
PETER JAMES QUINN

Don't select against trees showing insect damage

Lots of native leaf-eating insects live on pohutukawa. The species is home to a large community of invertebrates, most of which have a very close relationship with their host. Insects are generally only damaging to the tree's health when it is already sick.

Collecting seed

April and May are the best months to collect seed. Pick a dry day, hold a paper bag over a cluster of seed capsules and give it a good shake. This should produce thousands of tiny seeds. Alternatively, put a sheet on the ground and tap the branches with a long stick. Pohutukawa seed is very fine and very itchy and can take several washes to get out of your clothes.

Left: Seed heads.
BRET MCKAY

Storage

Pohutukawa seeds lose their viability quickly – when absolutely necessary, store them temporarily in the refrigerator (but not the freezer).

Propagation

- Prepare a number of shallow seedling trays. Fill to 50 millimetres (two inches) with sterilised seed raising mix or leaf–mould and loam (finely sieved and free of weeds).

- Sow the seed thinly on the dampened raising mix. Thick sowing can cause the seedlings to rot. You will want at least one centimetre between each seedling.

- Cover the seed very thinly with fine sand – the seeds should be just barely covered. Make sure the sand is from a river, not from the coast.

- Cover the tray with a sheet of plastic or glass and put two layers of newspaper over the top to keep the seedlings out of direct light.

- Check from seven days on. As soon as germination starts, remove the glass and paper and water lightly (with a fine mist spray). Keep the soil just moist. Don't over–water.

- Keep the seedlings in a sheltered spot out of the wind, direct sun and away from frost.

- At about three months, the seedlings should be around one centimetre high with four to six leaves. At this stage, prick them out into separate containers (a good chance to recycle plastic yoghurt and margarine containers).

- The planting mixture should be a commercial potting mixture or a leaf/loam mixture with added fertiliser.

- Pot into large containers as the plants grow.

- Trees need to be grown for two years before planting out. During the growing period, prune the lower twigs for easier handling later on.

Waikawau lagoon, Coromandel Peninsula.
PETER JAMES QUINN

Bret McKay

The Mimiwhangata Peninsula, one of Northland's most beautiful spots, is steadily becoming more so under the care of a gang of friends committed to restoring its forest to health. The Mimi-whangata Restoration Group (soon to be a Trust) primarily owes its existence to the vision and determination of Bret McKay, full-time salesman and passionate photographer of pohutukawa.

However, Bret doesn't just photograph and admire. He has spent years growing plants, particularly natives, from seeds and cuttings. And the ingenuity he and his fellow group members have brought to bear on the problems confronting them testify to a generous measure of Kiwi nous.

When the 330-hectare coastal park came into the hands of the Department of Conservation, its native cover was down to a few remnants. These are a small but key resource in the restoration process, providing the group with cuttings for its early plantings. 'They're important for two reasons,' Bret explains. 'Cuttings have adult foliage from the beginning, making them hardier than seedlings. And by taking them from older trees on the land we can be sure we are preserving genetic integrity. We would like to move to seeds eventually to bring in the diversity.'

They are developing seedlings by pollinating hardy trees with the pollen from heavy nectar producers and vice versa. The nectar is an important issue, as one of the objectives of the group is to promote trees which support birds, and plants which support those trees, such as flax and ngaio. Both shelter young trees and are a ready food source, the flax through its flowers, and ngaio through the insect life which thrive in it.

Early on the group established a small, automated nursery on the property which houses a few thousand plants. 'It means that plants become established in local conditions,' says Bret. In addition to pohutukawa they are raising rata for planting in the valley, the bush climber *Metrosideros carminea*, coastal maire, the large-leafed milk tree *(Streblus banksii)*, tawapou, and a variety of other coastal species.

The group has developed a sure-fire tree-growing recipe which is so successful that new plantings have endured eight rainless weeks in summer without any sign of stress.

Above: Bret McKay.
ROGER GRACE

Left: Little Barrier Island.
BRET MCKAY

Bret's 'sure to rise' pohutukawa recipe

The main plant enemies of pohutukawa are grasses, particularly kikuyu. Broadleaf weeds may look unsightly but don't seem to cause seedlings too much trouble.

- In kikuyu, don't spot spray – the roots will come back. Keep stock out for a year, let the kikuyu grow rank, then blanket spray with Roundup (glyphosate). It will collapse to form a mulch.

- Where there is moderate shelter, plant pohutukawa straight away.

- In fully exposed coastal sites, plant a semicircle of flax and ngaio, wait two years until they are two metres high, then plant the pohutukawa.

- The best time to plant is late Autumn when the ground is still warm, promoting good root growth. The shorter days mean the tops don't grow too much.

- In sandy soil plant deep with a small amount of Crystal Rain.

- Mulch 50 millimetres deep by one metre across.

- Drive a stake on either side of the tree and slide a 20-litre bucket with the bottom cut out down the stakes. Mulch heavily outside the bucket. The bucket keeps rabbits out and the sun and wind off the root zone.

- Keep the bucket in place for a maximum of two years, then slide it up the stakes and tie the tree to the stakes. By this stage it will have outgrown the rabbits' browsing zone.

References

No ordinary tree

1. Grey, Sir G. 1928: *Nga mahi a nga tupua*. 3rd Edition. p 94. New Plymouth, Thomas Avery.

2. Riley, M. 1994: *Maori Healing and Herbal: New Zealand Ethnobotanical Sourcebook*. p 355. Viking Sevenseas.

3. Colenso, W. 1865: *On the Geographic and Economic Botany of the North Island of the New Zealand Group.* Transactions and Proceedings of the New Zealand Institute. p 35.

4. Kirk,T. 1869: *On the Botany of the Thames Goldfields.* Transactions and Proceedings of the New Zealand Institute.

Botany

1. Simpson, P. G. 1994: *Pohutukawa and Biodiversity.* Conservation Advisory Science Notes No. 100. Department of Conservation. Wellington. p 2.

Pohutukawa and the forest ecosystem

1. Gabi Schmidt-Adam/Tony Whitaker, personal comment.

Vanishing glory

1. Forest Research Institute. 1989: *Tackling the Pohutukawa Health Problem. What's New in Forest Research.* No. 178. Rotorua. p 2.

2. Simpson, P. G. 1994: *Pohutukawa and Biodiversity.* Conservation Advisory Science Notes No. 100. Department of Conservation. Wellington. p 10.

Bibliography

Burstall, S.W. and E.V. Sale. 1984: *Great Trees of New Zealand*. Wellington, Reed.

Cockayne, L. and E. P. Turner. 1967: *The Trees of New Zealand*. Wellington. Government Printer.

Conly, G. and M. Conly. 1988: *New Zealand Pohutukawa*. Wellington, Grantham House.

Dawson, J. 1988: *Forest Vines to Snow Tussocks: the Story of New Zealand Plants*. Wellington, Victoria University Press.

Dunn, M. 1991: *A Concise History of New Zealand Painting*. David Bateman / Craftman House.

Hosking, G.P. 1993: *Seeing is not Believing: Insects as Symptoms not Causes*. New Zealand Entomologist. Volume 16.

Hutcheson, J. and G. Hosking. 1991: *Conservation of Pohutukawa*. Part 1, Insects associated with pohutukawa. Forest Health Research Group, Forest Research Institute, Rotorua.

Metcalf, L.1995: *The Propagation of New Zealand Native Plants*. Auckland. Godwit.

Orbell, M. 1991: *Hawaiki, a New Approach to Maori Tradition*. Christchurch, Canterbury University Press.

Smith, S. *Bibliography of Pohutukawa and Rata*. Unpublished. Project Crimson.

Whitaker, A.H. 1987: *The Roles of Lizards in New Zealand Plant Reproductive Strategies*. New Zealand Journal of Botany 25 (2).

Glossary

Canopy — The uppermost layers of leaves.

Epiphyte — Perching plant. Epiphytes are not parasitic and are generally beneficial to their hosts, for example, by storing water.

Invertebrate — Any creature without a backbone.

Lianes — Climbing or twisting plant.

Marsupial — A mammal belonging to the order Marsupialia. Young are generally suckled and carried in a pouch in the mother's belly. Best known examples are kangaroos and possums.

Rupestral — Rock dwelling tree or shrub.

Tapu — Sacred.

Tomentose — Hairy. A former name for pohutukawa was *M. tomentosa*, a reference to its hairy leaves.

Vertebrate — Any creature with a spinal column, including mammals, birds, reptiles, amphibians and fishes.

Waka — Maori canoe.

Index

Any school, organisation or individual wanting to know more about the Trust's work or how to apply for funding should contact:

The Project Crimson Trust
PO Box 17121
Greenlane, Auckland
New Zealand

Project
Crimson

Supported by Carter Holt Harvey Limited
& the Department of Conservation.